FRIEDRICH KUHLAU

FOUR SONATINAS

OP.88

Edited by Lionel Salter

THE ASSOCIATED BOARD OF
THE ROYAL SCHOOLS OF MUSIC

INTRODUCTION

In the most indirect way possible, Friedrich Kuhlau (1786-1832) owed his musical successes to Napoleon. He had been born near Hanover, but at the age of 14 he moved with his father, a military bandsman, to Hamburg, where (after losing an eye in an accident) he studied music with a pupil of C.P.E. Bach and Kirnberger, gave piano recitals and published his first compositions (songs, flute pieces and a piano sonata). In 1810, however, to avoid being conscripted into the French army when Napoleon invaded Hamburg, he fled to Copenhagen, where he rapidly made a name as a pianist and composer, playing his own concerto before the Queen. Two years later he received an appointment as court chamber musician, in 1813 he became a Danish citizen, and subsequently various operas of his were performed at the Royal Theatre, where for a short time he was also chorus-master. He had a considerable following in Sweden as a concert pianist and teacher; and he twice visited Vienna, where he spent a convivial evening with Beethoven (whose music he championed), exchanging impromptu canons with him. Sadly, in the last years of his life a fire in his house destroyed all his unpublished manuscripts, including a second piano concerto.

His piano sonatinas, intended for his pupils, have remained popular for more than 150 years, though they have often suffered from the attention of over-zealous editors who have indulged their own ideas about dynamics and even about notes. The present edition of Op.88 has been carefully based on the original 1827 publication in Copenhagen, the only differences being the addition of phrasing (which was almost entirely lacking), and metronome marks, and the revision of fingering.

LIONEL SALTER
London, 1989

Sonatina in C

Allegro [♩ = 132]

KUHLAU, Op.88 No.1

AB 2150

4

il basso leggiero

6

RONDO
Allegro [♩ = 116]

Andante cantabile [♩ = 72]

RONDO
Vivace [♩. = 72]

Sonatina in A minor

Op.88 No.3

Allegro burlesco [♩ = 120]

AB 2150

Sonatina in F

Allegro molto [♩. = 108]

Op.88 No.4

Rondo alla Polacca [♩ = 112]

Processed and printed by
Halstan & Co. Ltd., Amersham, Bucks., England